Please return this book on or before the date shown above. To
renew go to www.essex.gov.uk/libraries, ring 0845 603 7628 or
go to any Essex library.

Jenny's Choice
Text copyright © Margaret Adams 2012
Illustrations copyright © Ian Bobb 2012
Edited by Catherine White

First published and distributed in 2012 by Gatehouse Media Limited

ISBN: 978-1-84231-082-3

British Library Cataloguing-in-Publication Data:
A catalogue record for this book is available from the British Library

Gatehouse Media Limited provides an opportunity for writers to express their thoughts and feelings on aspects of their lives. The views expressed are not necessarily those of the publishers.

Author's Thanks

I would like to thank my family for their support, my students for reading my stories and a special thank you to Amanda, who has waited a long time to find out what happened after *Pam's Secret.*

Chapter 1 - Jenny, the child

It seemed to Jenny that she had spent her whole life having to choose. She did not mean the easy, everyday choices like whether to have toast or cornflakes for breakfast. She had to make difficult choices – things she did not really want to choose.

Jenny could remember when she was seven years old. She had lived in a nice house with her mum and her dad. She was a bit spoiled really. If she wanted something, she could have it. She had lots of noisy toys. Every time Dad came home from work, he would give her a coin for her money box. For such a little girl, she had a lot of things and a lot of money.

She could remember the day everything changed. It was the first time she had been asked to make a difficult choice. She had come in from the garden. Everything looked like it always did. A joint of beef was sitting on the worktop. The bottle of olive oil was next to it. Some tinfoil had been torn off the roll and was covering the joint.

Mum and Dad were both in the kitchen. Mum was waiting for the kettle to boil. She looked like she had been crying. Her eyes looked very moist. Dad was very calm. He sat Jenny down at the table. He sat down beside her. He spoke to her in a very quiet and gentle voice.

"Jenny," he said, "Mummy and Daddy love you very much. But we don't love each other any more. We are not going to live with each other any more. You can choose who you live with."

How could she choose? She was seven years old. She loved them both. But in the end, she did not have to choose. Dad's new girlfriend did not want her to live with them. She stayed with her mum.

But none of this helped with the choice that Jenny had to make now.

Chapter 2 - Jenny, the worker

Jenny worked at the Asco Supermarket. She had worked there for about six months. It was a great place to work – or it had been.

Jenny did not have a good job before she went to work at Asco. She had worked in a grotty pub called the Crooked Crown. That was where she had met Greg. She did not like him when she first met him. She had thought he was a creep. He had been in the pub one night when a man who was very drunk had tried to grab her. This man had been giving her grief all evening. Jenny thought he was gross. He stank of grease and his clothes were grimy.

When Jenny was collecting dirty glasses, this man had grabbed her and crushed her against a wall. He was trying to kiss her. Greg had stopped him. She liked Greg after that.

Greg told her he was the boss in Asco. He offered
her a job. She thought she would like that job better
and she would see Greg every day. Greg told her
not to tell anyone they were seeing each other.

Jenny did not like secrets, but Greg said it could make things difficult at work. It all made sense when he said it. Anyway, Jenny was crazy about him by now. He would leave her little notes written in crayon. When she worked on the dairy counter, she would find them by the cream. When she was stacking the shelves, she would find them by the crisps or the crackers.

But maybe she was right when she had first met him. Maybe he was a creep.

But none of this helped with the choice that Jenny had to make now.

Chapter 3 - Jenny, the keeper of secrets

Jenny knew that she had not liked Greg when she first met him because he looked a bit like Cliff. Cliff was her stepfather. For a long time after Mum and Dad split up, it was just Mum and Jenny in the house. Dad and his new girlfriend moved away to Cleveland. She hardly ever saw him. The house was so gloomy after Dad left. It was as though a big cloud hovered over Mum. Sometimes she would catch Mum watching the clock at about the time Dad used to come home. They both missed him.

Then one day Mum met Cliff. She had joined a club for people who wanted to get slim. It was in the Community Centre. Cliff was the caretaker there. One night when Mum went to the slimming club, he was putting some new glass in a broken window. She said that he had a gleam in his eye when he gave her back the glove that she had dropped. From that day Mum changed.

Suddenly, the gloom was gone. She never saw Mum
work as hard as she did the first night Cliff came for
tea. She cleaned until the house glistened. She put
away all the clean clothes that had been sitting on

a chair since they were ironed. She even cleared away the photographs of Dad from the living room. Then she put on some make-up. She brushed her hair until it gleamed. She almost looked glamorous, like those photos of famous people in magazines. She glowed.

It was not long until Cliff moved in. Jenny was glad to see her mum so happy. Then one night her mum had to go away. Grandma was ill and needed some help. It would only be for a few days and Cliff would look after her. But Cliff did not look after her. Cliff made her do things that you should not do with a small child. He told her that if she told anybody, they would think she was lying. Who would believe the claims of a little girl? He told her that her mum would be unhappy again.

She did not know what to do. Should she tell or should she keep it secret? It was a horrible choice for a little girl. It was the last time she ever kept a secret - until Greg.

But none of this helped with the choice that Jenny had to make now.

Chapter 4 - Jenny, the lover

Jenny sat down in a chair by the fire. She remembered lying in front of the fire with Greg – coal glowing in the flames. It was a lovely evening.

Today though, things had changed for Jenny. She had really believed Greg when he had said that he loved her. She had really believed him when he had said that they should not tell anyone at work because it might cause problems in the shop. She remembered when he had said it – they had been out for a picnic. They had been sitting under a big oak tree. They were sitting on her coat because the grass was a bit damp. They had driven off the road to this quiet spot. There had been a horse and her foal just over the hedge. After a while, they had thrown bits of a loaf to ducks in the river nearby. Then they had thrown twigs, watching them float along with the flow of the river.

She had wanted to tell Pam, her friend at work, about Greg. He told her not to. Jenny wished she had not listened to him. She could do with a friend right now. But Jenny had had to choose, and she chose Greg.

Jenny sipped her cocoa and nibbled on a piece of toast. She didn't have to choose Greg now. Would Pam forgive her?

She picked up the phone and dialled Pam's number. She cleared her throat and began to speak.

Chapter 5 - Jenny, the friend

Jenny had met Pam on her first day at Asco. Greg had asked Pam to take care of her and show her the ropes. Pam had been pleased to help.

In many ways they were not alike, but they had become friends quite quickly. Pam was plump; Jenny was slim. Pam was plain; Jenny was pretty. You could overlook Pam; you would notice Jenny.

It did not matter – they laughed at the same things and liked each other.

Jenny did not know that Pam had a crush on Greg, at least not to start with. Pam had told her one day when they were in the shop. Lily, one of the cleaners, overheard. Soon everyone knew.

Pam really believed that Jenny had told everyone. Jenny had let her think that – it was too difficult to have a friend who fancied your boyfriend! She had chosen Greg again.

She hoped Pam would help her with the choice she had to make now.

Chapter 6 - Jenny, the decision maker

Today had been a day for finding out.

Today Jenny had found out that Greg was married.
She had found out when she went to the office at
work and found him in there with his wife.

Today she had found out that Greg had children – a
little boy and a little girl. They had been in the office
with their mum. She hadn't said anything about her

and Greg. She hadn't said anything to his wife. She hadn't said anything to his children. There are things you don't want to know about your dad and the fact that he'd got a girlfriend was one of them.

Today she had found out she was pregnant. That was why she had been going to the office to see Greg. She thought he might be pleased. She wasn't sure, but she had thought he loved her. In the end, she didn't tell him. She just walked away.

Today she had found out the meaning of friendship, when she phoned Pam and told her. Pam had come round straightaway. There was no mention of the past, just friendship.

She told Pam she didn't know what to do. The choice was hard – have the baby or have a termination. She hated that word – terminate – it sounded like the Daleks. But to have a baby… it seemed such a big decision and she felt so alone.

She talked to Pam about the choice she had to make. She talked and Pam listened.

And in the end, she made the choice that was best for her.

Jenny's choice.

THE END

A comprehensive set of tutor resources, mapped to the Adult Literacy Core Curriculum, is available to support this book:

Jenny's Choice Tutor Resources CD-Rom
ISBN: 978-1-84231-083-0

Author's Note

I have written short stories for individual students on quite a few different occasions, usually to help them practise a particular letter pattern, consonant blend, digraph etc., or to meet an observed need of the particular student.

Jenny's Choice is the fourth title in the Supermarket Stories series. It was originally written for students within English Workshop, a literacy class within the ACRES consortium in East Sussex.

The main intention of the series is to give Entry level students a story to read. I have often found that books for students at this level don't always have a story as such, and, as someone who enjoys stories, I wanted to give my students the same opportunity. I wanted to show that reading can be a pleasure, not just a necessity.

They are adult stories with adult themes. I have written them so that students can read a chapter per session and I have finished each chapter at a point that will encourage the reader to come back for more.

Each chapter can be used to practise specific learning aims, although this does not have to be the case. The supporting resources also check comprehension and encourage the reader to think more broadly about the text. I hope that this will encourage the reader to see the relevance of reading stories - *they make you think, not just read.*

Margaret Adams

If you have enjoyed this book, why not try one of these other titles from Gatehouse Books:

Pam's Secret   ISBN: 978-1-84231-050-2
by Margaret Adams

The first book in the Supermarket Stories series. Pam shares a secret with Jenny, her new friend at work. Will Jenny betray Pam's trust?

Bob's Problem   ISBN: 978-1-84231-056-4
by Margaret Adams

The second book in the Supermarket Stories series. Bob likes his job on the dairy counter, but his boss has other plans for him. Bob is forced to reveal his problem. Then one day, a shocking event puts Bob's life on the line.

Dan's Dinner   ISBN: 978-1-84231-064-9
by Margaret Adams

The third book in the Supermarket Stories series. Dan, a supermarket employee, is a refugee who has had terrible and sad things happen in his past. One day something happens that may well change his future.

Getting Better   ISBN: 978-1-84231-026-7
by Marie McNamara

Marie's desire to improve herself is driven by the desperate wish to give her children a better start in life. *Getting Better* is an inspiring read.

Gatehouse Books®

Gatehouse Books are written for older teenagers and adults who are developing their basic reading and writing or English language skills.

The format of our books is clear and uncluttered.
The language is familiar and the text is often line-broken, so that each line ends at a natural pause.

Gatehouse Books are widely used within Adult Basic Education throughout the English speaking world. They are also a valuable resource within the Prison Education Service and Probation Services, Social Services and secondary schools - both in basic skills and ESOL teaching situations.

Catalogue available

Gatehouse Media Limited
PO Box 965
Warrington
WA4 9DE

Tel/Fax: 01925 267778
E-mail: info@gatehousebooks.com
Website: www.gatehousebooks.com